MW00603578

Grandmother, I Want to Hear Your Story

A Grandmother's Guided Journal To Share Her Life & Her Love

Jeffrey Mason

You can view and answer the questions in this book at
hearyourstory.com.

This website can be accessed by using any computer, tablet,
or smartphone. Using hearyourstory.com will give you the
ability to use a keyboard to answer the questions in this
book and share your memories.

You will also be able to save your work and
print multiple copies of your responses to
give to your entire family.

Please note there is a small one-time charge to cover the
cost of maintaining the site.

HEAR YOUR STORY

"Grandmothers and roses are much the same.

Each is God's masterpiece with different names."

— Unknown

"Grandmas
don't just say
'that's nice'
-- they reel back
and roll their eyes
and throw up
their hands and smile.
You get your money's
worth out of
grandmas."

— Unknown

THIS BOOK BELONGS TO:

IT'S YOUR BIRTHDAY!

"It's such a grand thing to be a mother of a mother — that's
why the world calls her grandmother." — Author Unknown

What is your birthdate?

_____

What was your full name at birth?

_____

_____

Were you named after a relative or someone else of
significance?

_____

_____

_____

In what city were you born?

_____

Were you born in a hospital? If not, where?

_____

_____

_____

What was your height (length) and weight at birth?

_____

IT'S YOUR BIRTHDAY!

"As I learned from growing up, you don't
mess with your grandmother." — Prince William

Was your birth early, on-time, or late?

_____

_____

Did you have any health issues when you were born?

_____

_____

_____

What were your first words?

_____

_____

How old were you when you took your first steps?

_____

Do you know what kind of house your parents lived in when
you were born?

_____

_____

_____

Where did you sleep when you a newborn?

_____

_____

IT'S YOUR BIRTHDAY!
"Grandmas are moms with lots of frosting."
— Author Unknown

What stories have you been told about the day you were born?

_____

_____

_____

_____

_____

_____

_____

_____

_____

_____

_____

_____

_____

IT'S YOUR BIRTHDAY!
"A grandma's heart is a patchwork of love."
— Author Unknown

How did your parents describe what you were like as a baby?

_____

_____

_____

_____

_____

_____

_____

_____

_____

_____

_____

_____

_____

_____

_____

_____

FAMILY TREE

"To forget one's ancestors is to be a brook without a source, a tree without a root." — Chinese Proverb

My Mother's Great-Grandmother

My Mother's Great-Grandfather

My Mother's Grandmother

My Mother's Grandfather

My Mother's Mother

My Mother's Father

My Mother

FAMILY TREE

"With family, love is the oil that eases friction, the cement that binds us together, and the music that brings harmony." — Friedrich Nietzsche

My Father's Great-Grandmother

My Father's Great-Grandfather

My Father's Grandmother

My Father's Grandfather

My Father's Mother

My Father's Father

My Father

GROWING UP
"Every house needs a grandmother in it."
— Louisa Mae Alcott

What three words best describe you when you were a kid?

_____

_____

_____

Did you have a nickname when you were growing up? If yes, how did you get it?

_____

_____

_____

Who was your best friend in your elementary school days? Are you still in contact with them?

_____

_____

_____

Which television family most reminds you of your family?

_____

_____

When you were a kid, did you share a bedroom or have one to yourself?

_____

_____

GROWING UP

"If nothing is going well, call your grandmother."
— Italian Proverb

What were your regular chores?

_____

_____

_____

Did you get an allowance? If yes, how much was it?

_____

_____

What are a few things you about being a kid?

_____

_____

_____

_____

_____

_____

_____

_____

_____

GROWING UP

"What can you do to promote world peace?
Go home and love your family." — Mother Teresa

Did you have braces when you were a kid?

_____

What is your favorite book from your childhood or teen years?

_____

_____

_____

What was a typical Saturday like when you were a kid? What did you spend the day doing?

_____

_____

_____

_____

_____

_____

_____

_____

_____

GROWING UP

"Families are like branches on a tree. We grow in different
directions, yet our roots remain as one." — Author Unknown

What is a favorite childhood memory?

_____

_____

_____

_____

_____

_____

_____

_____

_____

_____

_____

_____

_____

_____

_____

GRANDMOTHER TRIVIA

"A grandma is warm hugs and sweet memories. She remembers all of your accomplishments and forgets all of your mistakes." — Barbara Cage

What is your favorite flavor of ice cream?

_____

How do you like your coffee?

_____

Which do you prefer: cake or pie?

_____

If you could live anywhere in the world for a year with all expenses paid, where would you choose?

_____

_____

_____

_____

How do you like your eggs cooked?

_____

What is your shoe size?

_____

How old were you when you got your first email address?

_____

What superpower would you select for yourself?

_____

_____

GRANDMOTHER TRIVIA

"Just about the time a woman thinks her work is done,
she becomes a grandmother." — Edward H. Dreschnack

Do you have any allergies?

_____

_____

_____

What is your biggest fear?

_____

_____

Preference: cook or clean?

_____

What would you order as your last meal?

_____

_____

_____

_____

What do you cook better than anyone else in the family?

_____

_____

_____

_____

THE TEENAGE YEARS

"Mother - that was the bank where we deposited
all our hurts and worries." — T. DeWitt Talmage

How did you dress and style your hair during your teens? Do
you have any pictures?

_____

_____

_____

_____

Did you hang out with a group of people or a small number
of close friends? Are any of you still in contact?

_____

_____

_____

Did you date in high school? Did you have any boyfriends in
your teen years?

_____

_____

What was a common weekend night for you during your teens?

_____

_____

_____

_____

THE TEENAGE YEARS

"Having a teenager can cause parents to wonder
about each other's heredity." — Author Unknown

What were your weekend nights like when you were in high
school?

_____

_____

_____

_____

_____

_____

Did you have a curfew?

_____

Did you date in your high school years?

_____

_____

Did you go to any school dances? What were they like?

_____

_____

_____

_____

_____

THE TEENAGE YEARS

"When all the dust is settled and all the crowds are gone, the things that matter are faith, family, and friends." — Barbara Bush

In what kind of car did you learn to drive?

_____

_____

Who taught you how to drive?

_____

_____

What did you like and dislike about school?

_____

_____

_____

_____

Did you have a favorite and least favorite subjects?

_____

_____

_____

What were your grades like during high school?

_____

_____

_____

_____

THE TEENAGE YEARS

"Education is what remains after one has forgotten
what one has learned in school." — Albert Einstein

Who did you eat lunch with?

_____

_____

_____

What school activities or sports did you participate in?

_____

_____

_____

_____

_____

What are a few favorite songs from your high school years?

_____

_____

_____

_____

_____

_____

_____

THE TEENAGE YEARS

"If nothing is going well, call your grandmother."
— Italian Proverb

Knowing all you know now, what advice would you give your teenage self?

_____

_____

_____

_____

_____

_____

_____

_____

_____

_____

_____

_____

_____

_____

THE TEENAGE YEARS

"The most important thing in the world is family and love."
— John Wooden

Write about a teacher, coach, or other mentor that had a significant impact on you when you were growing up.

_____

_____

_____

_____

_____

_____

_____

_____

_____

_____

_____

_____

_____

_____

_____

_____

THE TEENAGE YEARS

"Family is the most important thing in the world."
— Diana, Princess of Wells

Write about a favorite memory from your teenage years.

_____

_____

_____

_____

_____

_____

_____

_____

_____

_____

_____

_____

_____

_____

WHERE HAVE YOU LIVED?

"Home is the nicest word there is."
— Laura Ingalls Wilder

List the cities where you have lived during your lifetime.
Include the dates if you can remember them?

_____

_____

_____

_____

_____

_____

_____

_____

_____

_____

_____

_____

_____

_____

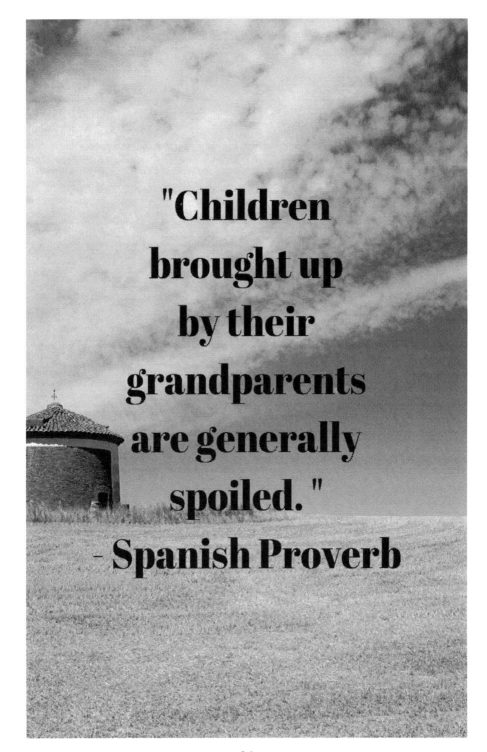

"Children brought up by their grandparents are generally spoiled."

- Spanish Proverb

"Young people
are raised
by their parents
but often led
by their
grandparents."
— Unknown

WHAT HAPPENED
THE YEAR YOU WERE BORN?

"Grandmas hold our tiny hands for just a little while
.... but our hearts forever." — Author Unknown

Google the following for the year you were born:
What historical events occurred?

_____

_____

_____

_____

_____

What movie won the Academy Award for Best Picture? Who
won Best Actor and Best Actress?

_____

_____

_____

What were a few popular movies that came out the year you
were born?

_____

_____

_____

_____

_____

WHAT HAPPENED
THE YEAR YOU WERE BORN?

"Grandparents make the world ... a little softer,
a little kinder, a little warmer." — Author Unknown

What song was on the top of the Billboard charts?

_____

_____

Who was the President of the United States?

_____

What were a few popular television shows?

_____

_____

_____

_____

What were the prices for the following items?
- A loaf of bread:
- A gallon of milk:
- A cup of coffee:
- A dozen eggs:
- The average cost of a new home:
- A first-class stamp:
- A new car:
- A gallon of gas:
- A movie ticket:

GRANDMOTHER TRIVIA

"Having somewhere to go is home. Having someone to
love is family. Having both is a blessing." — Author Unknown

Have you ever been told that you look like someone famous?
Who did they think you resembled?

_____

_____

_____

What is your morning routine?

_____

_____

_____

_____

_____

What is a favorite guilty pleasure?

_____

_____

_____

Have you ever broken a bone?

_____

_____

GRANDMOTHER TRIVIA

"The only rock I know that stays steady, the only
institution I know that works, is the family." — Lee Iacocca

Do you consider yourself to be an introvert or an extrovert?

_____

What is your favorite thing about yourself?

_____

_____

_____

_____

_____

Did you ever skip school when you were a kid?

_____

_____

If yes, what did you do during the time you should have
been in class?

_____

_____

_____

_____

_____

_____

PARENTS & GRANDPARENTS

"Children have one kind of silliness, as you
know, and grown-ups have another kind." — C.S. Lewis

Where was your mother born and where did she grow up?

_____

_____

_____

_____

What three words would you use to describe her?

_____

_____

_____

In what ways are you most like your mother?

_____

_____

_____

_____

_____

_____

_____

PARENTS & GRANDPARENTS

"When I was a boy, I thought my Grandmother lived in the kitchen. The stove was her kingdom, her church, and her medicine cabinet" — Author Unknown

Where was your father born and where did he grow up?

_____

_____

_____

_____

What three words would you use to describe him?

_____

_____

_____

In what ways are you most like your father?

_____

_____

_____

_____

_____

_____

_____

_____

PARENTS & GRANDPARENTS

"A moment lasts for seconds but the memory of it lasts forever."
— Unknown

What is a favorite memory of your mother?

_____

_____

_____

_____

_____

_____

_____

_____

_____

_____

_____

_____

_____

_____

_____

PARENTS & GRANDPARENTS
"We don't remember days, we remember moments."
— Unknown

What is a favorite memory of your father?

_____

_____

_____

_____

_____

_____

_____

_____

_____

_____

_____

_____

_____

_____

PARENTS & GRANDPARENTS

"Just when you think you know love, something little comes
along and reminds you just how big it is." — Author Unknown

What was your mother's maiden's name?

_____

Where was your mother's family from?

_____

_____

_____

Do you know your father's mother's maiden name?

_____

_____

Where was your father's family from?

_____

_____

_____

_____

How did your parents meet?

_____

_____

_____

_____

PARENTS & GRANDPARENTS

"Appreciate your parents. You never know what
sacrifices they went through for you." — Author Unknown

What three words would you use to describe their relationship.

_____

_____

_____

What were your parent's occupations?

_____

_____

_____

Did either of them have any unique talents or skills?

_____

_____

_____

_____

Did either of your parents serve in the military?

_____

_____

PARENTS & GRANDPARENTS
"Love is the chain whereby to bind a child to its parents."
— Abraham Lincoln

What is a favorite family tradition that was passed down from your parents or grandparents?

_____

_____

_____

What are a few of your favorite things that your mother or father would cook for the family?

_____

_____

_____

_____

What were grandparents like (your mother's parents)?

_____

_____

_____

_____

_____

_____

PARENTS & GRANDPARENTS
"Next to God, thy parents."
— William Penn

What were grandparents like (your father's parents)?

_____

_____

_____

_____

_____

_____

_____

Do you know where your mother's parents were born and grew up?

_____

_____

_____

_____

Do you know where your father's parents were born and grew up?

_____

_____

_____

_____

PARENTS & GRANDPARENTS

"There is no school equal to a decent home and no
teacher equal to a virtuous parent." — Mahatma Gandhi

What was the best advice your mother gave you?

_____

_____

_____

_____

_____

_____

_____

_____

_____

_____

_____

_____

PARENTS & GRANDPARENTS

"A father's goodness is higher than the mountain,
a mother's goodness deeper than the sea." — Japanese Proverb

What was the best advice your father gave you?

_____

_____

_____

_____

_____

_____

_____

_____

_____

_____

_____

_____

_____

_____

PARENTS & GRANDPARENTS

"A moment lasts for seconds but the memory of it lasts forever."
— Author Unknown

Did you meet your great-grandparents on either your mother or father's side? If yes, what were they like?

_____

_____

_____

_____

_____

_____

_____

_____

_____

_____

_____

_____

_____

PARENTS & GRANDPARENTS

"Grandmother — a wonderful mother with lots of practice."
— Author Unknown

What other individuals had a major role in helping you grow up?

_____

_____

_____

_____

_____

_____

_____

_____

_____

_____

_____

_____

_____

_____

_____

_____

BECOMING A MOM

"Pretty much all the honest truth telling there is
in the world is done by children." — Oliver Wendell Holmes

How old were you when you first became a mother?

_____

Who was the first person you told that you were going to be
a mom?

_____

_____

_____

Is there a specific song you would sing to your kids when
they were little?

_____

_____

What is the biggest difference in how kids are raised today
and when you raised your kids?

_____

_____

_____

_____

_____

_____

BECOMING A MOM

"If at first you don't succeed, try doing it the way
mom told you to in the beginning." — Author Unknown

Is there anything you would change about how your kids
were raised?

_____

_____

_____

_____

_____

_____

_____

_____

_____

_____

_____

_____

_____

_____

_____

BECOMING A MOM

"The soul is healed by being with children."
— Fyodor Dostoevsky

What is the biggest difference in your childhood and that of kids today?

_____

_____

_____

_____

_____

_____

_____

_____

_____

_____

_____

_____

_____

_____

BECOMING A MOM
"We are born of love; love is our mother."
— Rumi

Knowing what you know now, what advice would you give yourself as a new mother?

"It is as grandmothers that our mothers come into the fullness of their grace."
- Christopher Morley

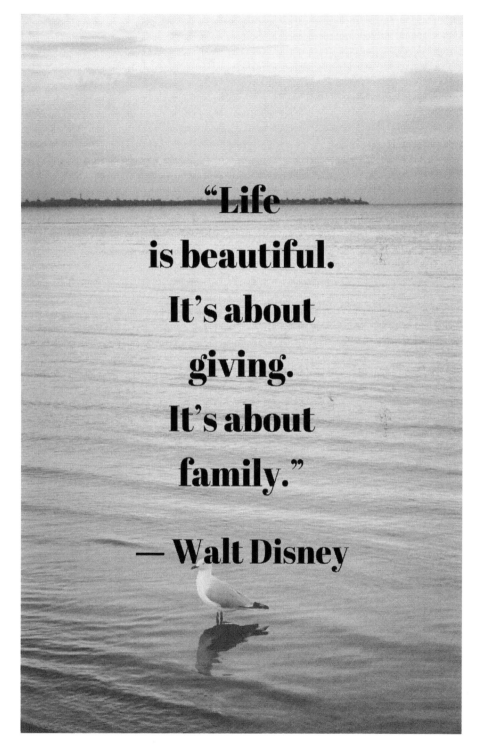

"Life is beautiful. It's about giving. It's about family."

— Walt Disney

YOUR SIBLINGS

"Brothers and sisters are as close as hands and feet."
— Vietnamese Saying

Were you the oldest, middle, youngest, or an only child?

_____

The following questions cover brothers and sisters. If you don't have siblings, feel free to talk about cousins or friends who were as close to you.

How many siblings do you have?

_____

List your siblings' names in order of their ages. Make sure to include yourself.

_____

_____

_____

_____

_____

Which of your siblings were you the closest with growing up?

_____

_____

Which of your siblings are you the closest in your adult years?

_____

_____

YOUR SIBLINGS

"The greatest gift our parents ever gave us was each other."
— Author Unknown

How would you use to describe each of your siblings when they were kids?

_____

_____

_____

_____

_____

_____

How would you use to describe each of your siblings as adults?

_____

_____

_____

_____

_____

_____

_____

YOUR SIBLINGS

"First a brother, then a bother, now a friend."
— Author Unknown

What is a favorite memory of each of your siblings (this
question is also on the next few pages to give you more
room if you need it)?

_____

_____

_____

_____

_____

_____

_____

_____

_____

_____

_____

_____

_____

_____

_____

YOUR SIBLINGS

"What causes sibling rivalry? Having more than one kid."
— Tim Allen

What is a favorite memory of each of your siblings?

_____

_____

_____

_____

_____

_____

_____

_____

_____

_____

_____

_____

_____

_____

_____

_____

YOUR SIBLINGS

"Siblings know how to push each other's buttons, but they also
know how to mend things faster than anyone." — Author Unknown

What is a favorite memory of each of your siblings?

_____

_____

_____

_____

_____

_____

_____

_____

_____

_____

_____

_____

_____

_____

_____

YOUR SIBLINGS

"The advantage of growing up with siblings is that
you become very good at fraction." — Author Unknown

What is a favorite memory of each of your siblings?

_____

_____

_____

_____

_____

_____

_____

_____

_____

_____

_____

_____

_____

_____

_____

_____

GRANDMOTHER TRIVIA

"My grandmother is the person who inspires me the most."
— Victoria Azarenka

What is your favorite season of the year?

_____

What do you listen to when you are alone in the car?

_____

_____

Do you ever buy lottery tickets?

_____

If yes, what is the largest amount of money you have won?

_____

_____

What is a smell that reminds you of your childhood? What is the memory that comes to mind?

_____

_____

_____

_____

_____

What name would you choose if you had to change your first name?

_____

GRANDMOTHER TRIVIA

"Gratitude is the sign of noble souls."
— Aesop

How old were you the first time you voted?

_____

If you could do any one thing for a day, what would it be?

_____

_____

_____

What is your least favorite household chore?

_____

_____

_____

What is a favorite memory from the last twelve months?

_____

_____

_____

_____

If you could only eat three things for the next year with no harm to your health, what would you pick?

_____

_____

_____

LET'S TALK ABOUT YOUR KIDS

"The best academy is a mother's knee."
— James Russell Lowell

What would your kids have been named if they were born the opposite gender?

_____

_____

_____

_____

_____

Who did your children most look like when they were babies?

_____

_____

_____

_____

_____

What were your kids' first words?

_____

_____

_____

_____

_____

LET'S TALK ABOUT YOUR KIDS

"The longest road out is the shortest road home."
— Irish Proverb

How old were they when they took their first step?

_____

_____

_____

How many of your children were planned and how many were "surprises?"

_____

_____

_____

Is there a specific book you remember reading to your kids?

_____

_____

_____

When your kids were babies, what trick did you use to calm them when they were upset?

_____

_____

_____

_____

LET'S TALK ABOUT YOUR KIDS

"Adults are just outdated children."
— Theodore Geisel

What are the ways your kids like you?

_____

_____

_____

_____

_____

_____

_____

_____

_____

_____

_____

_____

_____

LET'S TALK ABOUT YOUR KIDS

"Hugs can do great amounts of good, especially for children."
— Diana, Princess of Wales

How are they different?

_____

_____

_____

_____

_____

_____

_____

_____

_____

_____

_____

_____

_____

_____

LET'S TALK
ABOUT YOUR GRANDKIDS

"Grandparents are a delightful blend of laughter, caring deeds, wonderful stories, and love." — Author Unknown

What was your age when you became a grandmother?

_____

How many grandkids do you have?

_____

What are your grandkids' names?

_____

_____

_____

How were you told that you would be a grandmother? What was your reaction when you heard the news?

_____

_____

_____

_____

_____

_____

_____

_____

LET'S TALK
ABOUT YOUR GRANDKIDS

"I think when I became a grandmother my life changed
a lot, and I think I changed personally." — Carine Roitfeld

What do you remember about the first time you held your first
grandchild?

_____

_____

_____

_____

_____

_____

_____

_____

_____

_____

_____

_____

_____

_____

LET'S TALK
ABOUT YOUR GRANDKIDS

"Grandma always made you feel she had been waiting to see
just you all day and now the day was complete." — Marcy DeMaree

What is the most surprising thing about being a grandmother?

_____

_____

_____

_____

_____

_____

_____

_____

_____

_____

_____

_____

_____

_____

LET'S TALK
ABOUT YOUR GRANDKIDS

"A grandmother is a little bit parent, a little
bit teacher, and a little bit best friend." — Author Unknown

How is being a grandmother different than being a mother?

_____

_____

_____

_____

_____

_____

_____

_____

_____

_____

_____

_____

_____

_____

"One
of life's
greatest joys
is holding your
baby's baby."

— Author Unknown

"Parents know a lot, but grandparents know everything."

— Author Unknown

SPIRITUALITY & RELIGION
"Grandmothers sprinkle stardust over children's lives."
— Author Unknown

Were your parents religious when you were growing up?

_____

_____

_____

_____

How did they express and demonstrate their spiritual beliefs?

_____

_____

_____

_____

Do you pray? If yes, how often?

_____

_____

_____

Which has the most impact on our lives: fate or free will?

_____

_____

_____

SPIRITUALITY & RELIGION

"Grandmothers are just antique little girls."
— Author Unknown

What do you believe is the purpose of life?

_____

_____

_____

_____

_____

_____

_____

How have your religious beliefs and practices changed over the course of your life?

_____

_____

_____

_____

_____

_____

_____

_____

SPIRITUALITY & RELIGION

"The smallest seed of faith is better than the
largest fruit of happiness." — Henry David Thoreau

Do you regularly attend a formal religious service?

_____

_____

_____

What religious or spiritual practices do you incorporate into
your daily life?

_____

_____

_____

_____

_____

What do you do when times are challenging, and you need to
find additional inner strength?

_____

_____

_____

_____

_____

SPIRITUALITY & RELIGION

"Faith is a living, daring confidence in God's grace, so sure and certain
that a man could stake his life on it a thousand times." — Martin Luther

Do you believe in miracles? Have you experienced one?

_____

_____

_____

_____

_____

Write about a time you found relief from forgiving someone.

_____

_____

_____

_____

Do you believe that religion and spirituality should be a
smaller or larger part of the law and government policy?

_____

_____

_____

_____

_____

WORK & CAREER

"Family: where life begins and love never ends"
— Author Unknown

When you were a kid, what did you want to be when you grew up?

_____

_____

_____

What was your first job? How old were you?

_____

_____

How many jobs have you had during your lifetime? List a few of your favorites.

_____

_____

_____

_____

What is your least favorite job that you have had?

_____

_____

_____

WORK & CAREER

"Rejoice with your family in the beautiful land of life."
— Albert Einstein

If you were to open your own business, what kind of business would it be?

_____

_____

_____

What are three jobs you would never want to have?

_____

_____

_____

Is there a job or profession your parents wanted you to pursue? What was it?

_____

_____

_____

If every job paid the same and you could select the one you wanted, what profession would you want to do?

_____

_____

_____

_____

LOVE & ROMANCE

"If I know what love is, it is because of you!"
— Hermann Hesse

Do you believe in love at first sight?

_____

_____

Do you believe in soulmates?

_____

_____

What age were you when you went on your first date?

_____

What did you do on that date?

_____

_____

_____

How old were you when you had your first steady relationship?

_____

Did you have any celebrity crushes when you were young?

_____

_____

_____

LOVE & ROMANCE

"The best thing to hold on to in life is each other."
— Audrey Hepburn

Were you ever in a relationship with someone your parents did not approve?

_____

_____

Have you ever written someone a love poem or song or had one written for you?

_____

If yes, write a few lines that you may remember.

_____

_____

_____

_____

_____

What are five things you consider to be romantic?

_____

_____

_____

_____

_____

LOVE & ROMANCE

"If I had a flower for every time I thought of you, I
could walk through my garden forever." — Alfred Tennyson

What is a song that brings back romantic memories?

_____

_____

_____

Which is more romantic: a candle lit dinner or a picnic in the
park?

_____

_____

In what ways do you think your parent's relationship has
influenced how you have approached love and marriage?

_____

_____

_____

_____

_____

_____

_____

LOVE & ROMANCE

"You are my heart, my life, my one and only thought."
— Arthur Conan Doyle, *The White Company*

What are the five most important qualities of a successful relationship?

_____

_____

_____

_____

_____

Write about a favorite romantic moment.

_____

_____

_____

_____

_____

_____

_____

_____

_____

_____

TRAVEL

"Once a year, go someplace you've never been before."
— Dali Lama

Do you have a valid passport?

_____

Do you consider yourself to be a light or heavy packer?

_____

_____

What is the longest distance you have ever traveled? Where did you go?

_____

_____

_____

_____

How do you feel about cruises?

_____

_____

Do you enjoy long road trips in the car?

_____

_____

How do you feel about flying?

_____

_____

TRAVEL
"Life is short, and the world is wide."
— Author Unknown

When you travel, do you prefer to have a preplanned agenda, or do you decide what to do after you arrive?

_____

_____

_____

What is a favorite travel memory?

_____

_____

_____

_____

_____

_____

_____

_____

_____

_____

_____

_____

TRAVEL BUCKET LIST

"Man cannot discover new oceans unless he has
the courage to lose sight of the shore." — Andre Gide

List the top ten places you would visit if money and time were no concern.

1. _____

_____

2. _____

_____

3. _____

_____

4. _____

_____

5. _____

_____

TRAVEL BUCKET LIST

"The world is a book, and those who do not
travel read only one page." — Saint Augustine

Continued

6. _____

_____

7. _____

_____

8. _____

_____

9. _____

_____

10. _____

_____

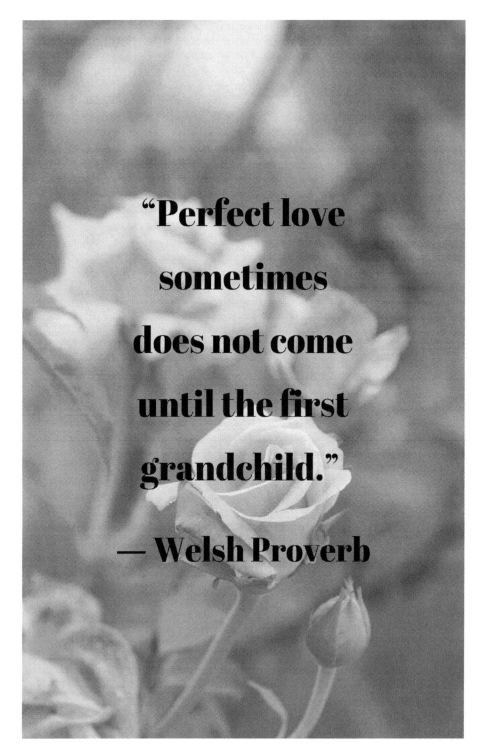

"Perfect love sometimes does not come until the first grandchild."

— Welsh Proverb

"Becoming
a grandmother
is wonderful.
One moment
you're just a mother.
The next you are
all-wise and historic."

— Pam Brown

TRIVIA

"Life is really simple, but we insist on making it complicated."
— Confucius

What would be the title of your autobiography?

_____

_____

Do you think you could still pass the written portion of the driver's test without studying?

_____

_____

What is your favorite color?

_____

What is your favorite quote or religious scripture?

_____

_____

Do you believe in life on other planets?

_____

_____

If you could travel through time, would you choose to meet your ancestors or your descendants?

_____

_____

_____

TRIVIA

"Gratitude is not only the greatest of virtues, but the parent of all others
— Cicero

What is your definition of success?

_____

_____

_____

_____

_____

What are five things you are grateful for?

_____

_____

_____

_____

_____

If you were forced to sing karaoke, what song would you perform?

_____

_____

_____

_____

_____

MOVIES, MUSIC, TELEVISION, & BOOKS

"A garden of love grows in a grandmother's heart."
— Author Unknown

What is the movie that you have watched the greatest number of times?

_____

_____

_____

What movie or television show can you remember loving when you were a kid?

_____

_____

_____

What actors and actresses would you cast to play yourself in the movie of your life? How about the rest of your family?

_____

_____

_____

_____

_____

MOVIES, MUSIC, TELEVISION, & BOOKS

"Life is a flower of which love is the honey."
— Victor Hugo

What are your favorite genres of music?

_____

_____

_____

_____

Which decades had the best music?

_____

_____

_____

_____

What is the first record (or cassette, cd, etc.) you can remember buying or being given as a gift?

_____

_____

_____

What song do you like today that would make your younger self cringe?

_____

_____

MOVIES, MUSIC, TELEVISION, & BOOKS

"Little souls find their way to you whether they're from your womb or someone else's." — Sheryl Crow

What is a song that reminds you of a special event or moment from your teen years?

_____

_____

_____

What song would you pick as the theme song of your life?

_____

_____

_____

What television show from the past do you wish was still on the air?

_____

_____

_____

If you could be cast in any television show or movie, past or present, which one would you choose?

_____

_____

_____

_____

MOVIES, MUSIC, TELEVISION, & BOOKS

"The way I see it, if you want the rainbow, you
gotta put up with the rain." — Dolly Parton

How has your taste in music changed over the years?

_____

_____

_____

_____

_____

What was the first concert you attended? Where was it held
and when did it occur?

_____

_____

_____

_____

What book or books have positively impacted the way you
think, work, or live your life?

_____

_____

_____

_____

_____

TOP TEN MOVIES

"Life is short, and it is here to be lived."
— Kate Winslet

List Your Ten Most Favorite Movies:

1. _____

2. _____

3. _____

4. _____

5. _____

6. _____

7. _____

8. _____

9. _____

10. _____

TOP TEN SONGS
"Where words leave off, music begins."
— Heinrich Heine

List Your Ten Most Favorite Songs:

1. _____

2. _____

3. _____

4. _____

5. _____

6. _____

7. _____

8. _____

9. _____

10. _____

TRIVIA

"When it seems the world can't understand,
your grandmother's there to hold your hand." — Joyce Logan

What is your favorite holiday?

_____

_____

Who would you invite if you could have dinner with any five people who have ever lived?

_____

_____

_____

Which ten-year period of your life is your favorite?
Examples include your 20's, 30's, 40's, etc. Why

_____

_____

_____

_____

_____

_____

TRIVIA

"Grandmas never run out of hugs or cookies."
— Author Unknown

What accomplishment are you most proud of yourself for achieving?

_____

_____

_____

_____

_____

Is there anything in your family's medical history that your kids should know about?

_____

_____

_____

_____

_____

Did you ever keep a diary or journal? If yes, any idea where it may be?

_____

_____

_____

_____

"Grandparents sort of sprinkle stardust over the lives of little children."

— Alex Haley

"Let me
love you
a little more
before
you're not little
anymore."

— Unknown

NOTES TO THOSE I LOVE

"So long as the memory of certain beloved friends live
in my heart, I shall say that life is good." — Helen Keller

This is space for you to write notes to your loved ones:

_____

_____

_____

_____

_____

_____

_____

_____

_____

_____

_____

_____

_____

NOTES TO THOSE I LOVE

"Life is all memory, except for the one present moment that goes by you so quickly you hardly catch it going." — Tennessee Williams

This is space for you to write notes to your loved ones:

_____

_____

_____

_____

_____

_____

_____

_____

_____

_____

_____

_____

_____

_____

_____

NOTES TO THOSE I LOVE

"The way you remember the past depends upon
your hope for the future." — Story Musgrave

This is space for you to write notes to your loved ones:

_____

_____

_____

_____

_____

_____

_____

_____

_____

_____

_____

_____

_____

_____

NOTES TO THOSE I LOVE

"Do not fear to be eccentric in opinion, for every opinion now accepted was once eccentric." — Bertrand Russell

This is space for you to write notes to your loved ones:

_____

_____

_____

_____

_____

_____

_____

_____

_____

_____

_____

_____

_____

_____

NOTES TO THOSE I LOVE

"Grandparents, like heroes, are as necessary
to a child's growth as vitamins." — Joyce Allston

This is space for you to write notes to your loved ones:

_____

_____

_____

_____

_____

_____

_____

_____

_____

_____

_____

_____

_____

_____

_____

NOTES TO THOSE I LOVE
"The smart, kind, beautiful child... must have
got it from their grandparents." — Author Unknown

This is space for you to write notes to your loved ones:

_____

_____

_____

_____

_____

_____

_____

_____

_____

_____

_____

_____

_____

_____

_____

NOTES TO THOSE I LOVE

"God's gift to us is our life; what we do
with it is our gift to him." — Author Unknown

This is space for you to write notes to your loved ones:

_____

_____

_____

_____

_____

_____

_____

_____

_____

_____

_____

_____

_____

_____

_____

NOTES TO THOSE I LOVE

"One must wait until the evening to see how
splendid the day has been." — Sophocles

This is space for you to write notes to your loved ones:

_____

_____

_____

_____

_____

_____

_____

_____

_____

_____

_____

_____

_____

_____

_____

_____

The Hear Your Story Line of Books

At **Hear Your Story**, we have created a line of books focused on giving each of us a place to tell the unique story of who we are, where we have been, and where we are going.

Sharing and hearing the stories of the people in our lives creates closeness, understanding, and strengthens our bond.

- Dad, I Want to Hear Your Story; A Father's Guided Journal to Share His Life & His Love

- Mom, I Want to Hear Your Story; A Mother's Guided Journal to Share Her Life & Her Love

- You Choose to Be My Dad; I Want to Hear Your Story: A Guided Journal for Stepdads to Share Their Life Story

- Life Gave Me You; I Want to Hear Your Story: A Guided Journal for Stepmothers to Share Their Life Story

- Because I Love You: The Couple's Bucket List That Builds Your Relationship

Available at Amazon and all Bookstores
hearyourstory.com

The Hear Your Story Line of Books

- Grandmother, I Want to Hear Your Story: A Grandmother's Guided Journal to Share Her Life and Her Love

- Grandfather, I Want to Hear Your Story: A Grandfather's Guided Journal to Share His Life and His Love

- To My Wonderful Aunt, I Want to Hear Your Story: A Guided Journal to Share Her Life and Her Love

- To My Uncle, I Want to Hear Your Story: A Guided Journal to Share His Life and His Love

- Love Notes: I Wrote This Book About You

- Getting to Know You: 201 Fun Questions to Deepen Your Relationship and Hear Each Other's Story

- You, Me, and Us: 229 Fun Relationship Questions to Ask Your Guy or Girl

- Papá, quiero oír tu historia: El diario guiado de un padre Para compartir su vida y su amo

Available at Amazon and all Bookstores
hearyourstory.com

DEDICATION
TO MY GRANDMOTHERS

To Eula Story Mason: to be your grandchild was to be royalty! Each time I smell Juicy Fruit Gum, drink sweet tea, or cook fried chicken, you are there with me. I think of your smile, your delicate laugh, and your irresistible modesty.

You are always perfectly put together...not a hair out of place, a crisply ironed blouse and matching pastel pants. Never a negative word and an unwavering love of God.

What is missed on first glance is your quiet strength. You know endurance, you know what matters. You keep moving forward and always make things work.

To Vivian Hensley Niles: as a young boy I knew you as my granny, not realizing that you were the forerunner of today's modern woman.

You worked and you were an artist in the kitchen. You paid the bills, and you took care of your family. You had a million opinions and you shared them all.

You were proudly you.

I am grateful for your example of work hard but have fun and I aspire to match your boldness and your never-stop-stamina. Every pancake I flip, when I work in the garden, and when I listen to Texas Swing, you're there with your coffee cup close at hand.

Granny Mason and Granny Niles, I Love You.

VIEW THIS BOOK
WITH YOUR COMPUTER

You can view and answer the questions in this book at hearyourstory.com.

This website can be accessed by using any computer, tablet, or smartphone.

Using hearyourstory.com will give you the ability to use a keyboard to answer the questions in this book and share your memories.

You will also be able to save your work and print multiple copies of your responses to give to your entire family.

Please note there is a small one-time charge to cover the cost of maintaining the site.

HEAR YOUR
STORY

ABOUT THE AUTHOR

Jeffrey Mason has spent twenty-plus years working with individuals, couples, and organizations to create change, achieve goals, and strengthen their relationships.

He is fiercely committed to helping others understand that forgiveness is the greatest gift we can give others and ourselves and to remember that while we have eternity, we don't have forever.

His mission is to provide a way for every person to share the story of their life.

He would be grateful if you would help people find his books by leaving a review on Amazon. Your feedback helps him get better at this thing he loves.

You can contact him at hearyourstory.com or directly at hello@jeffreymason.com.

You can join his Facebook group at facebook.com/JeffreyMasonAuthor.

He would love to hear from you.

"Let us
be grateful
to people who
make us happy;
they are the
charming gardeners
who make
our souls
blossom."

— Marcel Proust